EASY READERS – ACTIVITY BOOKS

This series of simplified [...] approximately 600 word[...]

They are suitable for students between the ages of 12 and 16 who have studied English for about two years.

These books are particulary useful as support material for teachers of English as a second language, since they have been structured to encourage active reading: on the left-hand page there is the story, complete with explanatory notes in English, and on the right-hand page there are exercises which refer exclusively to the text opposite. In this way the student is obliged not only to make a thorough study of what he has read, but also to analyse the use of vocabulary, tenses, syntax, etc. and to reproduce it; in this way, his teacher (and he himself) are able to verify his comprehension. Hence the name Activity Book – all writing is done on the page. No extra paper. No copy-books. And no need to leaf through the book – all the student needs is there before his eyes.

Each exercise is complete with an example that makes it quite clear what the student has to do. Some exercises review his grammatical knowledge of the English language, others are just good fun. By the end of the book the student will know the story and should be able to recount it, too!

adaptation, exercises and notes
Elizabeth Scott

printed by
Techno Media Reference - Milano

© text, notes and exercises

La Spiga languages 1997 - MILAN

distributed by
Medialibri Distribuzione s.r.l.
via Plezzo, 36 - tel. (02) 21.57.240 - 20132 Milano

The Adventures of
Tom Sawyer

Mark Twain

Mark Twain (1835 – 1910), whose real name was Samuel Clemens, Spent his boyhood by the Mississippi and was always fascinated by this river which became one of the main themes in his writing. (His pen-name was, in fact, an expression used by the Mississippi riverboat pilots). He led an adventurous life travelling and Contributing to various newspapers.

He wrote many stories but the most famous are *"The Adventures of Tom Sawyer"* (1876) and *"The Adventures of Huckleberry Finn"* (1844).

TRUANT[1]

"Tom!"

There was no answer.

"Tom!"

Still no answer.

"Where's that boy gone? Tom!"

The old lady looked all round the room. She looked under the bed, but found only the cat.

"If I catch that boy…," she muttered[2] to herself.

She opened the door and looked out into the garden.

"Tom!" she shouted.

Then she heard a slight[3] noise behind her. She turned round just in time to catch the boy as he came out of a cupboard.

"And what have you been doing in there?"

"Nothing," said the the boy.

"Nothing! Look at your hands and your mouth! What is that stuff?"

"I don't know, Aunt."

"Well I know. It's jam. I've told you forty times that if you touched that jam I'd skin[4] you. Give me that stick."

"Look out, Aunt! Look behind you!"

The old lady turned round and Tom was out of the door in a flash, over the garden fence[5] and away.

"Damn that boy! Will I never learn? He's always playing tricks on me. And he seems to know just how far he can go, too. But I can't take a stick to him. I really can't. After all, he's my dead sister's boy. Ah well, he'll play truant today and I'll have to make him work tomorrow. It's hard to make the boy work on a Saturday but he hates work and I have to teach him a lesson."

Tom did, in fact, play truant and had a very good time, too. He got home just in time to help Jim, the coloured boy, saw[6] next day's wood. At least, he was there to tell Jim his latest adventures, while Jim sawed the wood.

At supper, Aunt Polly tried to trick Tom into confessing that he hadn't gone to school.

"It was rather hot today, wasn't it, Tom?"

"Yes," answered Tom, cautiously.

"Not so hot now, is it?"

"No." What was Aunt Polly trying to say, wondered[7] Tom.

1. Answer the questions.

a) Who is looking for Tom?

....

b) Where was Tom?

....

c) What was he doing?

....

d) What day of the week is it?

....

e) Is the old lady Tom's mother?

....

f) Has he got a mother?

....

2. Look at this:

"If I catch that boy .... "

"If I catch that boy *I'll skin him.*"

Now complete the following in the same way.

a) If Tom plays truant ....

....

b) If he steals the jam ....

....

c) If the teacher catches him ....

....

d) If you help me saw the wood.............................

....

e) If he's under the bed ....

....

f) If he gets to school late ....

....

---

1. truant : *when one stays away from school without a good reason.*

2. muttered : *spoke in a low voice.*

3. slight : *small.*

4. skin : *take off the skin, meaning* 'to beat'.

5. fence : *barrier usually made of wood.*

6. saw : *cut.*

7. wondered: *asked himself.*

"Didn't you feel like a swim?"

"We used the pump on our heads. Look, my hair is still damp[1]."

Tom thought he was safe.

"You didn't have to undo[2] your shirt collar where I sewed it, then."

Tom was confident[3], now. He opened his jacket. His collar was securely sewed.

"Oh Tom," said Aunt Polly. "You're a good boy really."

She was half sorry that she had been wrong about him and half glad that, for once, he had been obedient.

"But, Auntie," came a voice. It was Sidney, Tom's younger brother. "Didn't you sew Tom's collar with white cotton? Look! Now it's black!"

Tom was already running out of the door.

"I'll beat you for that, Sid," he shouted as he ran down the garden.

THE NEW BOY

Tom soon forgot that problem. He had something much more important on his mind. A black boy had just taught him how to whistle[4] and he wanted to practice. He wandered down the road, whistling. It was a summer evening and it wasn't dark yet. Suddenly he saw a stranger in front of him. In the poor little village of St Petersburg a newcomer was an impressive curiosity, and this one was especially interesting. He was taller than Tom and very well-dressed – too well-dressed for a week-day. He even had shoes on, although it was only Friday! The more Tom looked at him, the more badly dressed he felt, and the more superior. Neither boy spoke. They stared[5] at each other but did not speak or move. Finally, Tom said: "I can beat you!"

"I'd like to see you try."

"Well, I can."

"No you can't."

"Yes I can."

"You can't."

"I can."

"Can't."

A pause.

"Well?" said the stranger.

"What's your name?" asked Tom.

3. Complete the tag questions and give the answers.

e.g. Tom didn't go to school, ... ? ....

Tom didn't go to school, did he? No, he played truant.

a) It wasn't a cold day, ...?......................................
....

b) Tom's hair wasn't dry, ...? ....
....

c) He didn't say he went swimming, ...?..............
....

d) Tom's collar wasn't sewn with white cotton, ...?
....

e) Aunt Polly didn't use black cotton, ...? ....
....

f) Aunt Polly didn't notice the different cotton, ...?
....

4. Find the names of the following.

a) Tom's brother ....
b) Tom's aunt ....
c) The town where they live ....
d) The black boy who works for them ....

   Now write a sentence about each.
   ....
   ....
   ....
   ....

---

1. damp : *not dry.*
2. undo : *open.*
3. confident : *sure of himself.*
4. whistle : *make harmonious sounds through one's lips.*
5. stared : *looked for a long time.*

"None of your business."

"Well, I'll make it my business."

"Why don't you, then?"

"You think you're clever[1], don't you?"

"Cleverer than you! And look at that hat!"

"I dare you to knock it off."

"And then ?"

"I'll bounce a rock off your head."

"You're a liar[2]."

"You're another."

"You're afraid."

"I'm not."

Another pause.

Tom drew a line in the dust with his toe[3].

"If you step over that line, I'll beat you till you can't stand up."

The new boy immediately stepped over it.

"Now," he said. "Let's see you do it."

"Don't push me."

"Well, you said you'd do it. Why don't you do it?"

"For two cents I will do it."

The new boy took two coins out of his pocket and held them out with scorn[4].

Tom struck them to the ground.

In an instant the two boys were on top of each other, rolling and tumbling in the dirt, like two fighting cats. In a cloud of dust, Tom appeared sitting on top of the newcomer, beating him with his fists.

"Say 'enough'," he said.

The boy tried to get free. Tom went on beating him.

"Say 'enough'," he repeated.

At last the new boy managed[5] to speak.

"Enough," he said, weakly. Tom let him go and he ran off down the road with Tom laughing at him. But as soon as Tom turned away, a stone hit him in the back. Tom turned and chased the traitor[6] home. He stood at the enemy's gate for a long time but the boy stayed indoors, occasionally making faces at Tom from the window. Finally, the enemy's mother appeared.

"Get away, you horrid, vulgar boy!" she shouted.

Tom got home very late. He climbed in through the window but Aunt Polly was there waiting for him. His

5. Put the following into indirect speech.

e.g. "What's your name?" asked Tom.

Tom asked him what his name was.

a) "Why don't you do it?" asked the stranger.

....

b) "Where are you going?" Mary asked her uncle.

....

c) "Who are you?" Aunt Polly asked the stranger.

....

d) "What's the time?" Tom asked Sidney.

....

e) "Which is yours?" Ann asked Harry.

....

f) "How old are you?" the stranger asked Tom.

....

6. Now do the same with these sentences.

e.g. "Don't push me" said Tom.

Tom told the stranger not to push him.

a) "Go away" said Tom.

....

b) "Come here at once" Auntie said to Sidney.

....

c) "Don't eat that!" said the doctor to the boy.

....

d) "Take off your hat" the gentleman said to the young man.

....

e) "Brush your teeth three times a day" the dentist said to the girl.

....

f) "Don't open that window" the man said to the woman.

....

---

1. **clever** : *smart, astute.*
2. **liar** : *a person who does not tell the truth.*
3. **toe** : *the 'fingers' of the feet.*
4. **scorn** : *disdain, feeling that the other does not merit respect.*
5. **managed** : *succeeded.*
6. **traitor** : *one who does not respect the rules.*

clothes were in a terrible state.

"That boy's going to work really hard tomorrow," she promised herself.

PAINTING THE FENCE

It was Saturday and a lovely summer's day. Everyone was on holiday, everyone was happy. Well, almost everyone. Tom looked at the fence in front of him and the happiness left his heart. Thirty yards[1] long and nine feet[2] high! He began to paint and then stopped to compare his white streak[3] with the unending continent of unpainted fence. He sat down under a tree, discouraged. At that moment, he saw Jim skipping along with a bucket[4] of water. He had always considered boring the job of fetching[5] water from the village pump, but now it seemed much better than the job he had to do. You could take a long time and at the pump there were always lots of boys and girls.

"Hey, Jim," he called. Jim came over.

"How about swapping[6] jobs for a bit? I'll get the water and you do some painting."

"Oh no, Master Tom," said Jim. "I couldn't do that. Your aunt said that I must go and get the water and not stop for anyone. She said you would ask me to paint and she told me I had to do my own job."

"Never mind what she said," said Tom. "I won't be long. She'll never know."

"I daren't,Tom. She'll beat me."

"She won't. She never beats anyone. Look, I'll give you a marble[7]."

The temptation was too much for Jim. He put down his bucket.

But in another minute he was flying down the street again, his bottom hurting; Tom was busy painting and Aunt Polly was walking back to the house with a slipper[8] in her hand and a look of triumph on her face.

Tom's energy did not last long. He knew that the other boys would soon come along and tease[9] him about his work. He pulled all his precious belongings out of his pocket: some marbles, bits of toys, rubbish – nothing he could sell.

Suddenly an idea came to him. He began painting.

After a few minutes, along came Ben Rogers. He was skipping along, eating an apple, and making strange noises

7. **Find six adjectives in the text and write a sentence with each.**

e.g. "horrid" - The woman thought Tom was a horrid boy.

....

....

....

....

....

....

....

....

....

8. **Now find five verbs showing movement and make a sentence with each:**

e.g. 'run' - he went running down the street.

....

....

....

....

....

....

....

....

....

---

1. **thirty yards** : *approx. 30 metres.*
2. **nine feet** : *approx. 3 metres.*
3. **streak** : *line.*
4. **bucket** : *container for carrying water etc.*
5. **fetching** : *going and getting.*
6. **swapping** : *exchanging.*
7. **marble** : *small ball of glass.*
8. **slipper** : *soft shoe.*
9. **tease** : *make fun of.*

11

like a steamboat. He stopped when he saw Tom hard at work.

"Hey Tom!" he said. "I'm going swimming. Don't you wish you could come? But of course you prefer working, don't you?"

"Working?" asked Tom, without stopping. "What do you call working?"

"Well, that's work, isn't it?"

"Perhaps it is and perhaps it isn't. Anyway, it suits[1] Tom Sawyer."

"Don't tell me you like doing that?"

"I don't see why I shouldn't like it. It's not every day a boy gets the chance to paint a fence."

He continued painting and then stood back to admire his work. Ben came closer[2]. He took another bite of his apple. How Tom wanted that apple!

"Say, let me have a go, will you?" said Ben.

"Oh, I couldn't do that. My aunt Polly wouldn't like that. She's very particular about this fence. You really have to know how to do it. There aren't many people capable of doing it."

"Is that true? Oh, please let me try. Just a little."

"I can't,Ben. Really I can't. Even Sid isn't allowed[3] to do it."

"I'll give you the rest of my apple."

The next moment Tom was lying under the tree munching[4] the apple while Ben was happily painting the fence.

And when Ben was too tired to go on, there was Billy Fisher who did it in exchange for his knife; then Johnny Miller for a dead rat on a string. So the work went on, hour after hour.

By the middle of the afternoon, Tom was rich. Apart from the things mentioned above, he had twelve marbles, a key, a piece of chalk, a piece of blue glass, a tin soldier, two tadpoles[5], six fireworks, a kitten with only one eye, a dog-collar – but no dog – and lots of other useless objects. The fence had three coats[6] of paint on it and he had spent a nice relaxing day.

"It's not such a bad world after all," he said to himself.

He had discovered a great law of human action: in order to make a man desire something, it is only necessary to make it difficult to obtain.

9. Write a paragraph in your own words describing how Tom got the fence painted without doing it himsef.

....
....
....
....
....
....
....
....
....
....
....

10. Make a list of all the things Tom was given and write beside them 'useful' or 'useless' according to your opinion.

e.g. an apple - useful.

....
....
....
....
....
....
....
....
....
....
....

---

1. **suits** : *is good for*.
2. **closer** : *nearer*.
3. **allowed** : *permitted*.
4. **munching** : *eating noisily*.
5. **tadpoles** : *baby frogs*.
6. **coats** : *layers*.

TOM'S NEW LOVE

Aunt Polly was sitting snoozing[1], the cat on her lap, when Tom came in. She was surprised to see him; she had expected him to have deserted his work a long time ago.

"Can I go and play now, Auntie?" he asked.

"What? Already? How much have you done?"

"It's all done, Auntie."

"Don't lie[2] to me, Tom."

"I'm not lying, Auntie. Honest. It's all done."

Aunt Polly still did not believe him. She got up and went out to see for herself. When she saw the perfect white fence , her astonishment[3] was undescribable.

"Well, I never! You can certainly work when you want to! Yes, of course you can go and play."

She was so overcome[4] by the spendour of his work that she took him into the kitchen and gave him one of the best apples. As he was running down the garden, he saw Sid and managed to hit him with a few hard lumps of earth before disappearing over the fence.

"Just to teach him a lesson for telling about the black cotton," he said to himself.

Walking past Jeff Thatcher's house, he saw a new girl in the garden. She had long yellow hair and blue eyes and was dressed in a white summer dress. She was the most beautiful creature Tom had ever seen. A certain Amy Lawrence immediately vanished out of his heart; he thought he loved her more than anything else in the world – in fact, he had only won her a week ago. Then, for seven days, he had been the happiest boy alive. Now, in one instant, he forgot her completely. When this angel noticed him, Tom began showing off[5] in all sorts of ways to impress her – doing incredible gymnastic performances. Then he saw that she was going towards the house, but before going in, she turned and threw a flower over the fence. Tom ran to pick it up and put it inside his shirt, next to his heart, or, at least, next to where he thought his heart must be.

But he did not leave the fence. He remained there, hoping to see her at the window, but she did not appear.

After supper he went out again. But his heart was melancholy and he chose solitary places. He sat by the river and contemplated his flower. At ten o'clock, he was outside that house again. He climbed the fence, crawled[6]

11. Answer the questions.

a) Why was Tom's aunt astonished when she saw the fence?

....

b) Why did she give him one of her best apples?

....

c) Why did Tom throw some lumps of earth at his brother?

....

d) Why did Tom start doing gymnastics outside Jeff's house?

....

e) Why was Tom melancholy after supper?

....

f) Why did Tom arrive home very wet?

....

12. Write a sentence with each of these words, according to the text:

e.g. creature – *She was the most beautiful creature he had ever seen.*

dress - flower - heart - river - candle - bucket

....

....

....

....

....

....

....

....

....

---

1. **snoozing** : *sleeping lightly.*
2. **lie** : *say things that are not true.*
3. **astonishment** : *great surprise.*
4. **overcome** : *emotionally moved.*
5. **showing off** : *displaying one's abilities so as to impress another person.*
6. **crawled** : *went on hands and knees.*

15

through the plants, and stood under the upstairs window where a candle was glowing. He lay down on the grass and decided to die at her feet. Suddenly the window was opened by a maidservant who threw a bucket of water out. Tom arrived home completely soaked[1] but Sid did not dare say anything as he watched him crawl into bed.

MONDAY SICKNESS

Tom woke up miserable on Monday morning. He always woke up miserable on Monday mornings. It was the idea of a whole week of school; he almost wished there were no weekends because that made it even more difficult to go back into captivity.

He lay in bed and wondered what he could invent this time. He listened to his body but could find nothing wrong. A little tummy ache? No. Then he realized that one of his teeth was loose[2]. Good! He was just going to start groaning[3] when he thought that Aunt Polly would pull the tooth out and that would hurt. He looked for something else. Suddenly he remembered what the doctor had said about a certain problem with toes – sometimes one had to stay in bed for one or even two weeks. He pulled his right foot out and looked at it. One of the toes was really hurting. Tom began to groan. Sid continued to sleep peacefully. Tom groaned more loudly. No result.

Tom was aggravated.

"Sid! Sid!" he shouted, shaking his brother. This worked. Sid slowly woke up and yawned[4]. Tom resumed his groaning. Sid sat up.

"What's the matter, Tom?"

Tom moaned[5].

"Tom! Tom!" Sid began shaking him, an anxious look on his face.

"Don't touch me, Sid. Just leave me alone."

"What's the matter? I must call Auntie."

"No, don't do that. It'll pass. Don't call anyone."

"But I must! Don't groan like that, it's terrible. How long have you been like this?"

"Hours. Ouch! Don't touch me, Sid. You'll kill me."

"Oh, Tom! Why didn't you wake me?"

"I forgive you everything, Sid. When I'm gone…"

"You aren't dying[6] are you, Tom?"

13. Choose the correct word for the following sentences:

a) Tom woke up miserable .... *(five / six / seven)* days a week.

b) For Tom, going to school was like going to .... *(church / prison / hospital)*.

c) He coud not find anything wrong .... *(except / apart / yet)* a loose tooth.

d) He did not want his aunt to pull it out .... *(besides / because / why)* it would hurt.

e) Sid was sure that Tom's agony was .... *(real / true / honest)*.

f) Tom did not .... *(need / like / want)* Sid to tell Aunt Polly.

14. Say whether the following are *True* or *False*:

a)	Sid woke up as soon as Tom began groaning.	T	F
b)	Tom woke Sid by shaking him.	T	F
c)	Sid was not worried when he heard Tom moaning.	T	F
d)	Aunt Polly was not deceived by Tom.	T	F
e)	Tom really began to feel ill.	T	F

Now rewrite the false ones correctly.

....
....
....
....
....

---

1. **soaked** : *very wet.*
2. **loose** : *not well-fixed.*
3. **groaning** : *making loud noises showing great pain.*
4. **yawned** : *opened his mouth wide.*
5. **moaned** : *made soft noises showing great pain.*
6. **dying** : *coming to the end of life.*

Sid ran out of the bedroom and down the stairs.

"Aunt Polly! Come quickly! Tom's dying!"

"Dying?" answered Auntie. "I don't believe it."

But she went running upstairs anyway.

Tom was now beginning to feel quite ill, his groans were so convincing.

"What's the matter with you?" she gasped.

"Oh Auntie!" cried Tom. "My toe is mortified."

The old lady fell into a chair, laughing a little.

"Tom, what a fright you gave me. Now shut up at once and get out of bed."

Tom felt a bit silly.

"Well, it seemed mortified. It hurt so much that I forgot my tooth."

"Tooth, eh? What's wrong with your tooth?"

"One of them's loose and it aches awfully."

"No problem," answered Aunt Polly briskly. "Sid, get the cotton from my sewing-box."

"Please, Auntie! Don't pull it out. It's stopped hurting now. Please! I don't want to stay at home."

"Ah! So all this was because you wanted to skip[1] school. Well, you'll have your tooth out and you'll go to school!"

In fact, it all turned out quite well for Tom. On his way to school, the gap[2] in his mouth was the envy of all the other boys; no-one could spit like he could!

HUCKLEBERRY FINN

On his way to school, Tom met Huckleberry Finn, the homeless boy whose drunken[3] father had abandoned him and left town. Huck was envied by all the other boys because he was free to do what he liked, and hated by all the mothers because he was lazy[4], vulgar and lawless[5]. Of course, Tom was not allowed to play with him so, of course, he played with him whenever he could. Huck was always dressed in old, torn[6] clothes that were much too big for him, and an old hat. In the spring he was always the first boy to go without shoes, and in the autumn he was the last one to put them on. On fine nights he slept on doorsteps and when it was raining he slept in an empty barrel[7]. He did not have to go to school or to church and he could go fishing or swimming when he wanted. He knew more bad words than anyone else and used them,

15. **Write a summary in your own words describing Tom's attempt to stay away from school.**

....
....
....
....
....
....
....
....
....
....
....

16. **Describe Huckleberry Finn - his family, where he lived, what he did, how he dressed, where he slept.**

....
....
....
....
....
....
....
....
....
....
....

---

1. **skip** : *miss.*
2. **gap** : *hole.*
3. **drunken** : *alcoholic.*
4. **lazy** : *never wanting to work.*
5. **lawless** : *not respecting the law.*
6. **torn** : *ripped, in pieces* (to tear; tore; torn).
7. **barrel** : *large wooden container for wine.*

too! Tom admired him more than anyone.

"Hello, Huck," said Tom.

"Hi."

"What've you got there?"

"A dead cat."

"Where'd you get it?"

"Bought it."

"How much?"

"A blue ticket."

"What's a dead cat good for, then?"

"Curing warts[1]."

"Curing warts, eh? How d'you do it?"

"Well," began Huck, "you go to a graveyard where somebody bad has just been buried[2]. About midnight, the devil or two or three devils, come along to take him away. You don't see them, buut you can hear them – they sound like the wind, maybe you hear them talk, too. When they take the guy[3] away you throw the dead cat after them saying "Devil follow body, cat follow devil, warts follow cat, I've finished with you."

"Have you ever tried it?"

"No, but I'm going to, tonight. They buried old Horse Williams on Saturday."

"Yeah, but today's Monday."

"Devils don't come out on Sundays."

Tom paused for a minute.

"Can I come with you?" he asked.

"Yeah, if you're not afraid."

"Course I'm not afraid."

"OK, then. I'll call you at half past eleven."

"Make a meow like a cat."

"Sure."

SCHOOL

It was late by the time Tom reached the school-house, but he walked in boldly[4], hung his hat up and sat down at his desk.

"Thomas Sawyer!" came a loud voice.

Tom knew that when his name was pronounced in full it meant trouble[5].

"Sir!"

"Come up here. Now, why are you late again?"

Tom was about to tell a lie when he saw two long tails of

17. Put the following in the right order:

How to cure warts:

.... - Devils take away the body.

.... - Devils come, making noises like the wind.

.... - You cannot see them but you can hear them.

.... - You go to the graveyard with the cat.

.... - You find out where someone bad has recently been buried.

.... - You throw the dead cat after them.

.... - You get a dead cat.

.... - You say:

.... - Warts follow cat.

.... - Cat follow devil.

.... - Devil follow body.

.... - I've finished with you.

18. Find the words in the text which correspond to the following:

a) place where people are buried - ....

b) to put under the ground - ....

c) to go after someone - ....

d) the sound a cat makes - ....

e) to say something that is not true - ....

f) to look long and hard - ....

---

1. **warts** : *small hard growths on skin, like verrucas.*
2. **buried** : *placed under the ground.*
3. **guy** : *man.*
4. **boldly** : *courageously.*
5. **trouble** : *punishment.*

yellow hair and recognized the love of his life; and beside her was the only vacant place on the girls' side of the classroom.

He immediately said: "I stopped to talk to Huckleberry Finn."

The master stared at him. He couldn't believe his ears. The boy actually[1] had the courage to admit it!

"You did what?"

"I stopped to talk to Huckleberry Finn," repeated Tom.

"Thomas Sawyer, this is the most astounding[2] confession I have ever heard. Take off your jacket."

The master's arm worked on Tom until it was tired.

"Now, sir, go and sit with the girls!"

Laughter[3] went round among the boys, but this was exactly what Tom had wanted. He went and sat next to the most beautiful creature in the world. Of course, she turned her head away from him, and Tom pretended[4] to study his book; but when all attention left them, he began to look at her. She looked round, made a face, and then looked away. Tom placed a peach on the desk in front of her. She pushed it away. He pushed it back.

"Please take it – I've got more," he whispered[5].

Now he began to draw something on his book. The girl tried not to look but her curiosity was too strong.

"Let me see."

It was the picture of a house with a garden round it.

"It's nice," she said. "Now draw a man."

The man was bigger than the house but she did not comment on this. She just said, "I wish I could draw."

"It's easy," said Tom, "I'll teach you."

"Will you, really? When?"

"At noon[6]. Do you go home for lunch?"

"I'll stay if you do."

"Ok. What's your name?"

"Becky Thatcher. What's yours? Oh, I know, Thomas Sawyer."

"That's what they call me when they beat me. I'm Tom when I'm good."

He began writing something on his book.

"What are you writing?" asked Becky.

"Nothing."

"Yes, you are. Let me see."

"You'll tell."

19. Complete the sentences according to the text.

a) Tom told the truth because ....
....

b) To punish Tom, the schoolmaster ....
....

c) Becky pretended not to be interested in Tom but ....
....

d) Tom told Becky that he would ....
....

e) They arranged to spend ....
....

f) Becky wanted to see what ....
....

20. Make a list of all the things you have learnt about Tom's school.

e.g. *They don't go to school on Saturdays.*

....
....
....
....
....

Now compare with your school.

e.g. *We go to school on Saturdays.*

....
....
....
....
....
....

---

1. **actually** : *really*.
2. **astounding** : *incredible*.
3. **laughter** : *the sound of laughing*.
4. **pretended** : *made it seem that he was*.
5. **whispered** : *spoke very softly*.
6. **noon** : *12pm, midday*.

"No, I won't. I promise."

"Promise you won't tell anyone as long as[1] you live?"

"I promise. Let me see!"

"Oh, you don't really want to see."

"I do, I do!" Becky touched Tom's hand. Tom gradually revealed the words he had written: I love you.

"Oh, you bad thing!" she said, but her face turned red and she looked pleased.

At that moment, Tom felt a hand gripping[2] his ear and lifting him up. He was taken in this way across the room and placed on his own chair. Giggles[3] went round the class. Tom's ear hurt but his heart was jubilant.

THE AGONY OF LOVE

Tom could not concentrate for the rest of the morning (which was not unusual). He tried really hard but the confusion inside him was too great. In the geography class he turned lakes into mountains, mountains into rivers, rivers into continents, until everything was complete chaos. In the spelling class he made mistakes in the simplest words, and he messed up his reading in the reading class.

At last the school bell rang. He ran to Becky and whispered: "Put on your bonnet[4] and pretend you're going home. Go round the corner and then come back when the others have gone."

At last they were together, alone. They went into the school-house which was empty and sat down. Tom gave Becky his pencil and guided her hand across the page. They drew[5] a beautiful house.

After some time, they began to lose interest in art.

"Do you like rats?" asked Tom.

"No, I hate[6] them. Do you like chewing gum?"

"Yeah. I've got some. I'll let you chew it a bit, but you must give it back."

So they took it in turns to chew Tom's gum.

"Becky?"

"Yes."

"Were you ever engaged?"

"What's that?"

"Engaged to be married. You tell a boy that you won't ever have anybody but him – ever, ever, ever – and then

21. Answer the questions with short answers.

e.g.   Who loves Becky?   *Tom does.*

        Who can draw?   *Tom can.*

a) Who carries Tom across the classroom by his ear?

....

b) Who is in the schoolhouse at lunch-time?

....

c) Who hates rats?

....

d) Who has some chewing gum?

....

e) Who wrote 'I love you'?

....

f) What is easy?

....

22. Now turn the above sentences into tag questions.

e.g. *Tom loves Becky, doesn't he?*

      Tom can draw, can't he?

....

....

....

....

....

....

....

---

1. **as long as** : *for all the time*.
2. **gripping** : *holding firmly*.
3. **Giggles** : *suppressed laughter*.
4. **bonnet** : *hat*.
5. **drew** : *designed* (to draw; drew; drawn).
6. **hate** : *dislike intensely*.

you kiss, that's all. It's easy."

"Kiss? What do you kiss for?"

"Well, they always do that."

"Who?"

"People in love. Do you remember what I wrote?"

"Ye – yes."

"Say it."

"No, I can't. Not now."

"Shall I tell you?"

Becky paused. Tom put his arm round her and whispered in her ear.

"Now you say it," he said.

"Well, turn your face away so you can't see. And never tell anyone, promise."

"I promise."

Shyly[1], she whispered "I love you". Then she jumped up and ran around and around the classroom.

"Now it's all done, Becky. All except the kiss."

Tom chased her until he caught her. He kissed her red lips.

"There!" he said. "Now you're never going to love anyone but me and you won't marry anyone but me."

"And coming to school and going home, you must always walk with me – when no-one is looking."

"It's nice."

"Yeah, it's great. Me and Amy Lawrence…"

Tom immediately realized his mistake[2] but it was too late.

"Oh, Tom!" cried Becky. "I'm not the first girl you've been engaged to!"

She began to sob[3].

"Please don't cry, Becky! I don't like her any more honestly."

"You do! You love her!"

Tom tried to put his arm round her but she pushed him away and cried even more.

Tom marched outside. He hoped she would come out. After a while, he went back in.

"Becky," he pleaded,[4] "I only care for you."

No reply – only sobs.

He pulled out his best jewel: a brass[5] door handle. "Here," he said. "Please take this."

23. Insert the appropriate adverb in the following sentences. Choose from: *sadly, softly, happily, angrily, desperately, hopefully.*

a) "Oh Bill, I love you so much", she said ....

b) "Look what you've done! You've broken my toy", the boy shouted ....

c) "You don't love me, you love him!" he said ....

d) "Today we're going for a picnic", the children said ....

e) "I only care for you", he said ....

f) "Will you marry me?" he asked ....

24. Choose the appropriate word or phrase.

a) Becky told Tom to turn his face away because
   1. she was shy
   2. she didn't like him
   3. he had bad breath

b) Their engagement was going to be
   1. official   2. a secret   3. a joke

c) Becky was upset because
   1. Tom was engaged before
   2. she disliked Amy Lawrence
   3. she didn't want to get engaged

d) Tom wanted to give Becky his best jewel
   1. to impress her
   2. because he didn't want it any more
   3. to show his love for her

e) Tom didn't return to school that day because
   1. he hates school
   2. he was too unhappy
   3. he had to work for Aunt Polly

f) Becky cried
   1. for a short time   2. for a long time   3. all day

---

1. **shyly** : *timidly.*
2. **mistake** : *error.*
3. **sob** : *breathe irregularly and noisily while crying.*
4. **pleaded** : *begged, asked desperately.*
5. **brass** : yellow metal

27

But Becky knocked it on the floor.

Tom turned and walked out and over the hills and far away, and never went back to school that day.

Becky cried and cried but he did not come back.

AN ADVENTUROUS NIGHT

Tom and Sid went to bed at half past nine that night. Tom lay awake waiting impatiently for Huckleberry Finn to come. At last he heard the sound of a cat. He quietly climbed out of the window and jumped down. Together he and Huck ran away into the darkness. After half an hour's walking they came to the graveyard. It was overgrown with grass and weeds and the old tombstones[1] were falling down. The wind was moaning in the trees. Tom feared it was the spirits of the dead complaining[2] at being disturbed. They found the new grave and hid[3] behind some trees to watch. Soon they heard voices.

"What's that?" whispered Tom, terrified.

"It's them. They're coming! What'll we do?"

"I don't know. D'you think they'll see us?"

"They see better than cats! I wish I hadn't come!"

"If we keep perfectly still they won't see us."

The voices came nearer.

"But Tom, those are human voices!"

Out of the darkness they could just see three figures. One was carrying a lantern.

"Huck!" cried Tom, "look, that's old Potter!"

"You're right! And isn't that Indian Joe? I'd prefer devils to men like them!"

As the men came nearer they saw that the third was young Dr Robinson.

They had a barrow[4], a rope and two spades[5] and when they found the new grave they stopped. The doctor sat down while the other two began digging.

"Hurry up!" he said. "The moon might come out."

Tom and Huck could almost touch him. They held their breath, terrified. At last the men pulled out the coffin,[6] opened it and took out the body.

"Now, out with another five dollars!" said Indian Joe.

"But I've already paid you!" cried the doctor.

"Five more dollars or no body!"

Furious, the doctor hit the Indian in the face. He fell to the ground.

25. Find the ten hidden words.

S	P	I	R	I	T	D
T	O	M	B	H	K	I
A	H	I	D	E	J	G
B	A	R	R	O	W	N
Y	C	O	F	F	I	N
Z	A	P	B	O	D	Y
I	D	E	V	I	L	G

26. Now write a sentence with each

....

....

....

....

....,.........................

....

....

....

....

....

....

....

....

....

---

1. tombstones : *inscribed stones placed at the head of a grave.*
2. complaining : *lamenting.*
3. hid : *stayed out of sight (to hide; hid; hidden).*
4. barrow : *container with one wheel for carrying things.*
5. spade : *tool for digging.*
6. coffin : *box for dead bodies.*

"Hey!" shouted Potter. "Don't you strike my partner!"

He attacked the doctor. Indian Joe came to his senses, grabbed[1] Potter's knife and waited for the right moment. As the doctor hit Potter with the heavy headboard of the grave, Joe stabbed[2] him with the knife. The doctor fell on top of Potter, blood[3] spurting.[4]

At that moment clouds darkened the terrible scene and Tom and Huck ran away as fast as they could go. They did not stop until they got to[5] the village. At last, panting,[6] they reached an old empty barn, rushed inside and collapsed.

"Oh, Huck!" cried Tom as soon as he could speak. "What's going to happen? What if the doctor dies? Who do we tell?"

"Tell?" answered Huck. "We can't tell anyone! If Indian Joe finds out that we know, he'll kill us too!"

Tom thought for a bit.

"Hucky, are you sure you can keep mum[7]?"

"We've got to, Tom. Look, let's swear[8] on it."

"Ok. Let's hold hands and swear."

"No, not like that. This is too serious. We need blood here."

Tom nodded[9] gravely. He took a flat piece of wood, took out a pencil and began to write:

Huck Finn and Tom Sawyer swear they will keep mum about this and they wish they may drop dead if they ever tell.

Huck was filled with admiration for Tom's writing. "Now, the blood."

Tom got out his needle[10] and cotton and began to prick[11] his thumb. He squeezed[12] out a drop of blood and then another. After many squeezes he managed to sign his initials. Then Huck did the same. They buried the wood while chanting[13] some strange incantations and then started off for home.

"Does that really mean we'll never tell?" asked Tom.

"Of course," answered Huck. "If we tell, we'll drop dead, don't you know that?"

"Oh yes," said Tom slowly.

And that is how Tom Sawyer and Huckleberry Finn became life-long friends. They had many adventures together – too many to tell here.

27. Write the story of Tom and Huck's adventure in the graveyard

....

....

....

....

....

....

28. Here is a list of 12 adjectives – match them with the different characters in the story (2 adjectives for each person)

pretty
fussy
kind   Huck
severe   Becky
adventurous   Sid
romantic   Aunt Polly
blonde   The schoolmaster
lazy   Tom
silly
smart (intelligent)
strict
childish

  Write a sentence about each person, using the two adjectives.

....

....

....

....

....

....

---

1. **grabbed** : *took quickly.*
2. **stabbed** : *pushed the knife into.*
3. **blood** : *red liquid in the veins.*
4. **spurting** : *coming out fast.*
5. **got to** : *reached, arrived at.*
6. **panting** : *out of breath.*
7. **keep mum** : *keep a secret.*
8. **swear** : *make a solemn promise* (to swear; swore; sworn).
9. **nodded** : *moved his head meaning 'yes'.*
10. **needle** : *metal instrument for sewing.*
11. **prick** : *make a very small hole.*
12. **squeezed** : *pressed hard.*
13. **chanting** : *singing.*

EASY READERS - ACTIVITY BOOKS

IMPROVE YOUR ENGLISH
unabridged • parallel notes

AUDIO BOOKS 📼 EASY READERS

AUDIO BOOKS 📼 IMPROVE YOUR ENGLISH

POCKET CLASSICS
unabridged and complete

AUDIO BOOKS 📼 POCKET CLASSICS